M000087200

THE
ACCOMPLISHMENT
JOURNAL

THE ACCOMPLISHMENT JOURNAL

Job interviews, performance reviews, and an actionable tool kit for shining brighter than ever before

SYDNEY BAKER

SYDNEY BAKER

The Accomplishment Journal

Copyright © 2019 by Sydney Baker

First edition

ISBN: 978-1-9992719-0-9

All rights reserved under International and Pan-American Copyright Conventions. Manufactured in Canada and the United States.

No part of this publication may be reproduced, stored in or introduced into a retrieval system, or transmitted in any form or by any means (electronic, mechanical, photocopying, recording or otherwise) without the prior written permission of the publisher. This book is sold subject to the condition that it shall not, by way of trade or otherwise, be lent, resold, hired out, or otherwise circulated without the publisher's prior written consent in any form of binding, cover, or condition other than that in which it was published.

Disclaimer: the advice provided in this book is based on the author's personal experiences and opinions; it provides no guarantee for landing a job, promotion, or otherwise. This book is no more than a tool for keeping track of professional experiences that might prove useful down the line.

BOOK DESIGN Laura Wrubleski

EDITOR Kelsey Straight

PUBLISHING SUPPORT The Self Publishing Agency

THREE CORE BENEFITS

Imagine you're in a job interview and so far, it's going pretty well. Through random icebreaker conversation, you have already discovered a few things in common, and you haven't put your foot in your mouth yet. In fact, you are even communicating well. *Yes!*

After a while, the hiring manager brings up an experience-related question: *Can you tell me about a time when you demonstrated your resourcefulness?* You visibly smile as the question unfolds because yes, absolutely, you have utilized this skill 112,650 times. It's practically your biggest strength! Then panic hits... *Shit. They're done talking. Now I have to talk. Which example do I choose? Wait, why can't I think of anything? Nothing!? HOW IS THIS HAPPENING?*

Let's consider another scenario. It has now been one year since you began working for your current employer. At this point, you feel super proud of your accomplishments, having basically become the "go-to" person in your department. The time comes for an annual review, so you sit down with your manager, confident that they see your value and a raise is most definitely coming your way. The meeting goes well but reaches a close without any talk of compensation. *Should I say something? Wait until next year? Find a new job and avoid the discussion entirely?*

Heart pounding, you decide to blurt out a frantic request for more money. After a brief pause that feels like an eternity, your manager asks how much you want and what you've done to deserve the increase. Immediately, you freeze. *Because I do great work? Because I've put in extra hours every week since day one?*

Before going into these life-changing situations, wouldn't it be nice if you could quickly reference a roster of your most significant work experiences and achievements to date?

What if I told you that it only takes 10-15 minutes per week to make that a reality?

This journal provides a home for your professional triumphs until you're ready to leverage them for interviews, performance reviews, or job applications. Whether it be goal achievements, demonstrated initiative, self-improvement, or simply the utilization of valuable soft skills such as teamwork, you can keep track of it all!

In a moment, I will dive into the nitty-gritty of things, such as the various journal questions you'll encounter throughout the coming year, the obstacles you might face, and various tips on how to follow through week after week. First, let's get super clear on the many benefits you'll gain from this new journaling habit.

BENEFIT #1

OVERCOME A COMMON INTERVIEW "PAIN POINT"

Experience-related questions (more formally named "behavioral interview questions") are sneaky little things. To be clear, I'm talking about any sort of question that inquires about your past. For example:

> *When was the last time...*
> *Give me an example of...*
> *Have you ever...*
> *Tell me about a time when...*
> *What's the worst...*
> *Talk to me about...*
> *Can you recall...*

These questions draw out your past experiences (and actions) to predict how you'll handle similar situations in the future. They're basically the *mother lode* of interview questions; if answered properly, they also reveal little glimpses into your personality, values, temperament, and skill-set overall.

Unfortunately, behavioral interview questions are often met with a theoretical answer instead of a real-life example, which leaves the hiring manager a bit disappointed, wishing for more. So, how can you benefit from this intel?

01 Learn the answering framework

With behavioral interview questions, speaking from genuine experience is always the first step; next comes your ability to present the important details of that experience effectively.

As such, many use the "S.T.A.R. method" to structure their answers; this simple acronym focuses on the following four key components:

Describe the *Situation*, outline the corresponding *Task*, summarize your *Actions* to complete said task, and indicate the final *Result* of your efforts.

Ideally, choose an experience that is relevant to the role you are applying for and has a positive result.

02 Practice, practice, practice

New territory for you? Not to worry! Memorize the above framework and take it for a test drive. Perform a quick Google Search for *"behavioral interview questions [insert your industry]"* and talk through a couple of responses as if faced with a real interview. Then do it again. And again.

03 Gather your examples over time

It's one thing to recall *something, anything* on the spot when this type of question presents itself, but to have a refreshed memory of all your most significant work experiences before a big interview? That's magic.

So, take a moment out of each week to scribble down a few notes regarding your latest work adventures. What do you have to lose?

BENEFIT #2
ROCK YOUR PERFORMANCE REVIEWS

Asking for a raise can be hella' scary (correction: it *is* hella' scary), but sometimes reaching your financial goals means facing fear and discomfort head on. How can we enter these conversations with confidence and a greater likelihood to succeed?

Instead of leaving it up to your employer to piece together whether or not you deserve a promotion, make it a no-brainer! Show up for your performance review armed and ready to talk about your latest, greatest, and most valuable achievements.

For example, you could remind them of how you...

- Made a record-breaking sale last month (and the month before that...)
- Identified and fixed a bug in the company's product *before* it became a problem!
- Revamped an outdated process to be 80 percent more accurate, saving time and headaches.
- Stepped up to do something outside your job description when no one else would.

Okay, that's all great and everything, but when it comes time to actually prepare for said performance review, these things might mesh together as one big lump, perfectly summarized as: *I've worked my butt off; it's time for a freaking vacation!*

In an effort to put your best foot forward, take a moment out of each week and note what you've recently achieved, completed, or otherwise stepped up to the plate to accomplish. Your future self will thank you.

BENEFIT #3
POSITIVE SIDE EFFECTS: REFLECTION, GROWTH, AND GRATITUDE

Furthermore, there are a number of "bonus benefits" that come along with this journaling habit.

For example, at each checkpoint you will...

- Clear mental space by putting thoughts on paper, preparing your mind to move on to the next big thing.
- Switch focus to what you've learned from difficult situations, instead of dwelling on the negative.
- Feel a sense of progression and growth as you check in every week.

And over time you might...

- Notice a trend for what you're good at or want to avoid in the future.
- Reread your entries to remember the highs when you're feeling low.
- Acknowledge how much you've grown and evolved since day one.

Consider this: If you had the opportunity to see without a doubt that you're seriously kicking-ass in your career, would you take it?

WHAT TO EXPECT

You will encounter four different types of exercises throughout this journey: one set of *initial questions*, fifty-two sets of *weekly questions*, thirteen (yes, thirteen!) sets of *monthly questions*, and one set of *year-in-review questions*. In other words, this mighty little book will capture 365 days of your badass accomplishments!

INITIAL QUESTIONS

Let's kick things off with a bang. *What are your career goals, big or small? Where do you aspire to work? Which skills do you need to develop in order to be totally qualified?* Try to give the initial questions some serious thought, because it's helpful to reference your notes throughout the year as a reminder of what you're working towards.

WEEKLY QUESTIONS

Some situations may seem small or insignificant at the time, but you never know what sort of bizarre interview questions will arise down the line. That's why the weekly check-ins have been meticulously designed to cover the largest range of work experiences possible: from teamwork to problem solving, communication, and everything in between. Take a moment to reflect on what went particularly well and what did not, because the ability to learn and grow from difficult experiences (and mistakes!) is a valuable trait—one that many employers seek out.

MONTHLY QUESTIONS

Sometimes it's tough to see the big picture after just seven days, so immediately after each four-week cycle, you will be presented with an additional set of questions to tie up any loose ends. Take this time to get clear on what your absolute biggest accomplishments were over the last four weeks (and why). Tackle these questions immediately after you finish Week Four's journal entry. That way you're ready to start fresh during the next cycle.

Note: Since calendar months are not made up of perfect four-week chunks, there are thirteen cycles (a.k.a. "months") in this book.

YEAR-IN-REVIEW QUESTIONS

You did it! Congratulations on committing to this new habit for an entire year. That's huge! Let's take a moment to reflect, visualize how you've grown, and check in on your career goal progress.

OTHER RESOURCES

At the back of this book, you will find a collection of important soft skills and traits that are often brought up in interviews. Reference this list constantly, refreshing your memory and staying focused in your journal entries. *Want to take it one step further?* Highlight the soft skills that seem most applicable to you and your dream job.

SOFT SKILLS Personality traits, behaviors, and interpersonal abilities (typically obtained through life experience). E.g. communication, teamwork, adaptability, etc.

HARD SKILLS Technical abilities (typically obtained through some form of education). E.g. machine operation, Adobe Photoshop, fluency in a second language, etc.

OVERCOMING OBSTACLES

A few obstacles or excuses may come to mind as you read through this section, which by the way is totally normal. When it comes to major life changes, there will always be *something* standing in your way. Otherwise you'd be living the dream already! To help you out of this funk, let's discuss a few common roadblocks and how to shift your mindset in a positive direction.

I should have started five years ago. It's too late for me now.

Actually, quite the opposite! When it comes to behavioral interview questions, hiring managers are often looking to hear about recent examples opposed to ancient history. They might even specify a timeframe such as "in the last six months" or "in the last two years" depending on what they're looking for exactly. So, start this journaling habit *now*—right now! You will be working with a plethora of examples before you know it.

Still not convinced? Look at it this way: as you check in, week after week, you may find that certain situations spark your memory of prior situations. This is great news! Before those memories disappear into the void again, jot them down on the blank pages located at the back of this book.

My job is pretty repetitive. I won't have enough to write about.

Do you have co-workers to interact with every day? Productivity goals to achieve? How about customers to impress? Are there any extra tasks for you to take on?

Every day is an experience. Even if your work is more service-based than project-based, there must be *something* good that happens every week, in addition to something "meh" that holds a lesson. Do your best with what you've got and don't be discouraged if you can't fill out every question every time. Something is surely better than *nothing*.

I can hardly remember what I ate for breakfast yesterday.

In this day and age, we are constantly bombarded with information overload, forcing our brains to keep up as quickly as possible. With each passing moment, we file something into the deep dark corners of our memory archives. Alas, as the world evolves, our habits must too!

If you find that memory games are not your strong suit, figure out a way to make life easier on yourself. Chances are that you'll have an easier time remembering your latest experiences on a weekly basis, opposed to being put on the spot a few months (or years) into the future. In other words, this book was especially made for you!

If after a few tries, the weekly check-ins just aren't working out, don't give up. Simply adjust your frequency. If that means taking notes here and there throughout the week, instead of at a dedicated time once every week, great. This is your life, your future, your experience. Do what you need to succeed.

HOW TO COMMIT

Starting something is a big deal in itself, but actually sticking to it? That's the real challenge—so before embarking on this journey, take a moment to reflect on your earlier attempts to create new habits. If they fizzled out, what happened?

Here are a few tips and tricks on how to commit:

01   Pick a specific day and time for your journal entries every week. If possible, try for a weekday such as Thursday (or Friday, if you have the discipline...). This is your golden opportunity to transfer your thoughts onto paper and clear your mind. Get this done before the weekend and focus on recharging instead of obsessing over work!

02   Set a recurring reminder on your phone. If you're going to hit snooze, fine. Just don't turn the alarm off without this book already in hand. Go ahead and set up the reminder right now. (Seriously! I'll wait).

03   Store this book, plus a pen, in a central location. Sometimes, just making the effort to stand up and walk across the room is enough to derail you, so plan ahead!

04   Make a no-nonsense decision that you can afford to spend 10-15 out of the 10,080 minutes in every week to help your future-self succeed.

05 Identify your motivations and write them down somewhere accessible, such as your phone's note-taking app or on your bathroom mirror in bright lipstick letters (okay, maybe not the latter–but if that's your jam, go for it).

06 Treat yo' self. Plan out rewards for maintaining this habit following one month, three months, six months, and twelve months. You deserve it!

07 Get an accountability buddy. Have a friend check-in with you regularly (and vice-versa) to ensure that you're following through consistently.

Finally, go easy on yourself.

Some people thrive on structure and recommended processes; some people do not–that's the beauty of being human. We are all unique and shine in different ways. If following the rules is not exactly your forte, you have full permission (no, full encouragement!) to adapt this process however works best for you.

Every situation is different and follows its own timeline, so skip a question here and there if you need. Write five answers instead of one. Make your entries beautiful masterpieces, or simply scribble them down. If you miss a week, no worries. Catch up when you can and then keep going. Don't give up. This is for you. As long as you keep track of your work experiences and all that you've learned from them, one way or another, you're doing this right. And I am already so insanely proud of you.

Alrighty, that's my speech. Now let's get started!

INITIAL KICKOFF QUESTIONS

What are your current career goals? Feel free to think BIG or go small.

...Maybe you want to start your own company, make a certain amount of money,

obtain a specific job title, work in a particular field, etc.

_____

_____

_____

_____

_____

_____

What motivates you to reach these goals? List out absolutely everything that comes to mind.

...Being able to donate generously to a certain cause, becoming an impactful

team leader, having the opportunity to live your best-foodie life, the option to

work from home in your pajamas, etc.

_____

_____

_____

_____

_____

_____

What are your professional weaknesses? Be honest.

...Difficulty in staying organized, lack of focus, tardiness, etc.

_____

_____

_____

_____

_____

_____

_____

_____

What are you currently doing to overcome these weaknesses?

...The last 20 minutes of my day are reserved for updating my task-list and tidying

my work area.

_____

_____

_____

_____

_____

_____

_____

_____

_____

Go to Indeed or LinkedIn and find two job opportunities that align with your interests and career goals. Now, let's dig into your qualifications for each role.

OPPORTUNITY 01   Write the job title and company name here.
_____

What excites you most about this job?

...Prestigious employer, more opportunity for growth, higher salary, awesome office
_____

culture, etc.
_____

_____

_____

_____

_____

In what ways are you already qualified?

...College diploma, two years customer service experience, proficient in Excel, etc.
_____

_____

_____

_____

_____

_____

_____

In what ways could you become more qualified?

...Gain experience leading a team, obtain a particular certification, learn the basics of HTML, etc.

_____

_____

_____

_____

_____

_____

_____

What are the various "soft skills" noted in the job posting?

...Independence, adaptability, prioritization, organization, autonomy, etc.

_____

_____

_____

_____

_____

_____

_____

_____

_____

OPPORTUNITY 02 _____

What excites you most about this job?

_____

_____

_____

_____

_____

_____

_____

_____

In what ways are you already qualified?

_____

_____

_____

_____

_____

_____

_____

_____

_____

In what ways could you become more qualified?

_____

_____

_____

_____

_____

_____

_____

_____

What are the various "soft skills" noted in the job posting?

_____

_____

_____

_____

_____

_____

_____

_____

Bonus: Flip to the "soft-skills brainstorming page" at the back of this book; highlight the skills and traits that you've listed above, plus any others that seem relevant to your career.

WEEKLY & MONTHLY QUESTIONS

WEEKLY QUESTIONS

DATE / /

List two situations that you feel proud of this week, along with the corresponding soft skill(s) that you demonstrated.

Tip: Reference the "soft-skills brainstorming page" for a refresher!

SITUATION

SKILL(S)

01 My boss had a personal emergency, so I took over

Initiative

"Y" Project

_____

02

_____

What challenge or unexpected hurdle did you face this week?

...Perhaps your entire team called in sick (on the same day!), or software that you

frequently use went offline, or your client sent back what you thought was a

finished product for the zillionth time, etc.

Did you have a memorable and/or difficult interaction with someone? What happened?

...Maybe you fessed-up to a mistake, managed a wacky customer, informed a

client of an unfortunate delay in their project, etc.

\
\
\

Why are you grateful for this experience?

...Perhaps it taught you an important lesson, strengthened your patience, made

you realize something about yourself, etc.

\
\
\

In what way did you lend a helping hand, take on extra work, or otherwise go above and beyond?

...Maybe you dropped everything to deal with an urgent situation, took initiative to

train a new hire, cleaned the communal kitchen, stayed late after work to wrap

something up, picked up a co-worker's lunch, etc.

\
\
\

Is there anything else that you would like to make note of?

...The more the merrier!

\

WEEKLY QUESTIONS

List two situations that you feel proud of this week, along with the corresponding soft skill(s) that you demonstrated.

Tip: Reference the "soft-skills brainstorming page" for a refresher!

SITUATION   **SKILL(S)**

01 _____   _____

_____   _____

_____

_____

_____

02 _____   _____

_____   _____

_____

_____

_____

What challenge or unexpected hurdle did you face this week?

_____

_____

_____

_____

Did you have a memorable and/or difficult interaction with someone? What happened?

_____

_____

_____

_____

_____

Why are you grateful for this experience?

_____

_____

_____

_____

In what way did you lend a helping hand, take on extra work, or otherwise go above and beyond?

_____

_____

_____

_____

_____

Is there anything else that you would like to make note of?

_____

_____

WEEKLY QUESTIONS

List two situations that you feel proud of this week, along with
the corresponding soft skill(s) that you demonstrated.

Tip: Reference the "soft-skills brainstorming page" for a refresher!

SITUATION   **SKILL(S)**

01

_____   _____

_____   _____

_____

_____

_____

02

_____   _____

_____   _____

_____

_____

_____

What challenge or unexpected hurdle did you face this week?

_____

_____

_____

_____

Did you have a memorable and/or difficult interaction with someone? What happened?

_____

_____

_____

_____

_____

Why are you grateful for this experience?

_____

_____

_____

_____

_____

In what way did you lend a helping hand, take on extra work, or otherwise go above and beyond?

_____

_____

_____

_____

_____

Is there anything else that you would like to make note of?

_____

_____

WEEKLY QUESTIONS

List two situations that you feel proud of this week, along with the corresponding soft skill(s) that you demonstrated.

Tip: Reference the "soft-skills brainstorming page" for a refresher!

SITUATION   **SKILL(S)**

01
_____   _____

_____   _____

_____

_____

_____

02
_____   _____

_____   _____

_____

_____

_____

What challenge or unexpected hurdle did you face this week?

_____

_____

_____

_____

Did you have a memorable and/or difficult interaction with someone? What happened?

_____

_____

_____

_____

_____

Why are you grateful for this experience?

_____

_____

_____

_____

_____

In what way did you lend a helping hand, take on extra work, or otherwise go above and beyond?

_____

_____

_____

_____

_____

Is there anything else that you would like to make note of?

_____

_____

MONTHLY QUESTIONS

Describe a project, task, or situation that you are particularly proud of this month.

...Maybe you discovered a hazard and fixed it, achieved an excellent result, finally

completed a drawn-out project, dealt with a web-server crash at 2am, etc.

_____

_____

_____

_____

_____

_____

_____

_____

_____

_____

Can you tie a metric to something that you did or contributed to somehow?

...Maybe you produced an excellent result for your client, completed a record-breaking

number of projects, did something to save the company time or money, etc.

_____

_____

_____

What did you do that was out of your comfort zone?

...Perhaps you dealt with an angry customer, presented to senior management, asked someone for help, etc.

_____

_____

_____

_____

_____

Did you face an ambiguous situation? How did you move forward?

...Maybe you were told to organize the stockroom without any real instruction, or you were vaguely asked to "report on results," or you had an unresponsive client with a deadline fast approaching, etc.

_____

_____

_____

_____

Did you help someone to see a different angle, idea, or approach to a situation?

...Perhaps you showed a co-worker how to handle a tedious task more effectively, or you helped your boss to view a sensitive situation in a different light, or you talked a client out of a rather bad "big idea."

_____

_____

_____

_____

Is there anything else that you would like to make note of?

...The more the merrier!

_____

_____

WEEKLY QUESTIONS

List two situations that you feel proud of this week, along with
the corresponding soft skill(s) that you demonstrated.
Tip: Reference the "soft-skills brainstorming page" for a refresher!

SITUATION   **SKILL(S)**

01
_____   _____

_____   _____

_____

_____

_____

02
_____   _____

_____   _____

_____

_____

_____

What challenge or unexpected hurdle did you face this week?

_____

_____

_____

_____

Did you have a memorable and/or difficult interaction with someone? What happened?

_____

_____

_____

_____

_____

Why are you grateful for this experience?

_____

_____

_____

_____

_____

In what way did you lend a helping hand, take on extra work, or otherwise go above and beyond?

_____

_____

_____

_____

_____

Is there anything else that you would like to make note of?

_____

_____

WEEKLY QUESTIONS

List two situations that you feel proud of this week, along with
the corresponding soft skill(s) that you demonstrated.

Tip: Reference the "soft-skills brainstorming page" for a refresher!

SITUATION   **SKILL(S)**

01
_____   _____

_____   _____

_____

_____

_____

02
_____   _____

_____   _____

_____

_____

_____

What challenge or unexpected hurdle did you face this week?

_____

_____

_____

_____

Did you have a memorable and/or difficult interaction with someone? What happened?

_____

_____

_____

_____

_____

Why are you grateful for this experience?

_____

_____

_____

_____

_____

In what way did you lend a helping hand, take on extra work, or otherwise go above and beyond?

_____

_____

_____

_____

_____

Is there anything else that you would like to make note of?

_____

_____

WEEKLY QUESTIONS

List two situations that you feel proud of this week, along with the corresponding soft skill(s) that you demonstrated.

Tip: Reference the "soft-skills brainstorming page" for a refresher!

SITUATION   **SKILL(S)**

01
_____   _____

_____   _____

_____

_____

_____

02
_____   _____

_____   _____

_____

_____

_____

What challenge or unexpected hurdle did you face this week?

_____

_____

_____

_____

Did you have a memorable and/or difficult interaction with someone? What happened?

_____

_____

_____

_____

_____

Why are you grateful for this experience?

_____

_____

_____

_____

_____

In what way did you lend a helping hand, take on extra work, or otherwise go above and beyond?

_____

_____

_____

_____

_____

Is there anything else that you would like to make note of?

_____

_____

WEEKLY QUESTIONS

List two situations that you feel proud of this week, along with the corresponding soft skill(s) that you demonstrated.

Tip: Reference the "soft-skills brainstorming page" for a refresher!

SITUATION   **SKILL(S)**

01

_____   _____

_____   _____

_____

_____

_____

02

_____   _____

_____   _____

_____

_____

_____

What challenge or unexpected hurdle did you face this week?

_____

_____

_____

_____

Did you have a memorable and/or difficult interaction with someone? What happened?

_____

_____

_____

_____

_____

Why are you grateful for this experience?

_____

_____

_____

_____

_____

In what way did you lend a helping hand, take on extra work, or otherwise go above and beyond?

_____

_____

_____

_____

_____

Is there anything else that you would like to make note of?

_____

_____

Describe a project, task, or situation that you are particularly proud of this month.

_____

_____

_____

_____

_____

_____

_____

_____

_____

_____

_____

_____

Can you tie a metric to something that you did or contributed to somehow?

_____

_____

_____

_____

_____

What did you do that was out of your comfort zone?

_____

_____

_____

_____

_____

Did you face an ambiguous situation? How did you move forward?

_____

_____

_____

_____

_____

Did you help someone to see a different angle, idea, or approach to a situation?

_____

_____

_____

_____

_____

Is there anything else that you would like to make note of?

_____

_____

WEEKLY QUESTIONS

List two situations that you feel proud of this week, along with
the corresponding soft skill(s) that you demonstrated.

Tip: Reference the "soft-skills brainstorming page" for a refresher!

SITUATION   **SKILL(S)**

01
_____   _____

_____   _____

_____

_____

_____

02
_____   _____

_____   _____

_____

_____

_____

What challenge or unexpected hurdle did you face this week?

_____

_____

_____

_____

Did you have a memorable and/or difficult interaction with someone? What happened?

_____

_____

_____

_____

_____

Why are you grateful for this experience?

_____

_____

_____

_____

_____

In what way did you lend a helping hand, take on extra work, or otherwise go above and beyond?

_____

_____

_____

_____

_____

Is there anything else that you would like to make note of?

_____

_____

WEEKLY QUESTIONS

List two situations that you feel proud of this week, along with
the corresponding soft skill(s) that you demonstrated.
Tip: Reference the "soft-skills brainstorming page" for a refresher!

SITUATION   **SKILL(S)**

01
_____   _____

_____   _____

_____

_____

_____

02
_____   _____

_____   _____

_____

_____

What challenge or unexpected hurdle did you face this week?

_____

_____

_____

_____

Did you have a memorable and/or difficult interaction with someone? What happened?

_____

_____

_____

_____

_____

Why are you grateful for this experience?

_____

_____

_____

_____

_____

In what way did you lend a helping hand, take on extra work, or otherwise go above and beyond?

_____

_____

_____

_____

_____

Is there anything else that you would like to make note of?

_____

_____

WEEKLY QUESTIONS

DATE / /

List two situations that you feel proud of this week, along with
the corresponding soft skill(s) that you demonstrated.
Tip: Reference the "soft-skills brainstorming page" for a refresher!

SITUATION   **SKILL(S)**

01
_____   _____

_____   _____

_____

_____

_____

02
_____   _____

_____   _____

_____

_____

_____

What challenge or unexpected hurdle did you face this week?

_____

_____

_____

_____

Did you have a memorable and/or difficult interaction with someone? What happened?

_____

_____

_____

_____

_____

Why are you grateful for this experience?

_____

_____

_____

_____

_____

In what way did you lend a helping hand, take on extra work, or otherwise go above and beyond?

_____

_____

_____

_____

_____

Is there anything else that you would like to make note of?

_____

_____

List two situations that you feel proud of this week, along with the corresponding soft skill(s) that you demonstrated.

Tip: Reference the "soft-skills brainstorming page" for a refresher!

SITUATION   **SKILL(S)**

01 _____   _____

_____   _____

_____

_____

_____

02 _____   _____

_____   _____

_____

_____

_____

What challenge or unexpected hurdle did you face this week?

_____

_____

_____

_____

Did you have a memorable and/or difficult interaction with someone? What happened?

_____

_____

_____

_____

_____

Why are you grateful for this experience?

_____

_____

_____

_____

_____

In what way did you lend a helping hand, take on extra work, or otherwise go above and beyond?

_____

_____

_____

_____

_____

Is there anything else that you would like to make note of?

_____

_____

03 MONTHLY QUESTIONS

DATE   /   /

Describe a project, task, or situation that you are particularly proud of this month.

_____

_____

_____

_____

_____

_____

_____

_____

_____

_____

Can you tie a metric to something that you did or contributed to somehow?

_____

_____

_____

_____

_____

What did you do that was out of your comfort zone?

_____

_____

_____

_____

_____

Did you face an ambiguous situation? How did you move forward?

_____

_____

_____

_____

_____

Did you help someone to see a different angle, idea, or approach to a situation?

_____

_____

_____

_____

_____

Is there anything else that you would like to make note of?

_____

_____

WEEKLY QUESTIONS

DATE   /   /

List two situations that you feel proud of this week, along with
the corresponding soft skill(s) that you demonstrated.
Tip: Reference the "soft-skills brainstorming page" for a refresher!

SITUATION   **SKILL(S)**

01
_____   _____

_____   _____

_____

_____

_____

02
_____   _____

_____   _____

_____

_____

_____

What challenge or unexpected hurdle did you face this week?

_____

_____

_____

_____

Did you have a memorable and/or difficult interaction with someone? What happened?

_____

_____

_____

_____

_____

Why are you grateful for this experience?

_____

_____

_____

_____

_____

In what way did you lend a helping hand, take on extra work, or otherwise go above and beyond?

_____

_____

_____

_____

_____

Is there anything else that you would like to make note of?

_____

_____

WEEKLY QUESTIONS

List two situations that you feel proud of this week, along with the corresponding soft skill(s) that you demonstrated.

Tip: Reference the "soft-skills brainstorming page" for a refresher!

SITUATION

SKILL(S)

01 _____ _____

_____ _____

_____

_____

_____

02 _____ _____

_____ _____

_____

_____

_____

What challenge or unexpected hurdle did you face this week?

_____

_____

_____

_____

Did you have a memorable and/or difficult interaction with someone? What happened?

_____

_____

_____

_____

_____

Why are you grateful for this experience?

_____

_____

_____

_____

_____

In what way did you lend a helping hand, take on extra work, or otherwise go above and beyond?

_____

_____

_____

_____

_____

Is there anything else that you would like to make note of?

_____

_____

WEEKLY QUESTIONS

List two situations that you feel proud of this week, along with
the corresponding soft skill(s) that you demonstrated.

Tip: Reference the "soft-skills brainstorming page" for a refresher!

SITUATION   **SKILL(S)**

01
_____   _____

_____   _____

_____

_____

_____

02
_____   _____

_____   _____

_____

_____

_____

What challenge or unexpected hurdle did you face this week?

_____

_____

_____

_____

Did you have a memorable and/or difficult interaction with someone? What happened?

_____

_____

_____

_____

_____

Why are you grateful for this experience?

_____

_____

_____

_____

_____

In what way did you lend a helping hand, take on extra work, or otherwise go above and beyond?

_____

_____

_____

_____

_____

Is there anything else that you would like to make note of?

_____

_____

WEEKLY QUESTIONS

List two situations that you feel proud of this week, along with
the corresponding soft skill(s) that you demonstrated.
Tip: Reference the "soft-skills brainstorming page" for a refresher!

SITUATION   **SKILL(S)**

01
_____   _____

_____   _____

_____

_____

_____

02
_____   _____

_____   _____

_____

_____

What challenge or unexpected hurdle did you face this week?

_____

_____

_____

_____

Did you have a memorable and/or difficult interaction with someone? What happened?

_____

_____

_____

_____

_____

Why are you grateful for this experience?

_____

_____

_____

_____

_____

In what way did you lend a helping hand, take on extra work, or otherwise go above and beyond?

_____

_____

_____

_____

_____

Is there anything else that you would like to make note of?

_____

_____

DATE / /

Describe a project, task, or situation that you are particularly proud of this month.

_____

_____

_____

_____

_____

_____

_____

_____

_____

_____

Can you tie a metric to something that you did or contributed to somehow?

_____

_____

_____

_____

_____

What did you do that was out of your comfort zone?

_____

_____

_____

_____

_____

Did you face an ambiguous situation? How did you move forward?

_____

_____

_____

_____

_____

Did you help someone to see a different angle, idea, or approach to a situation?

_____

_____

_____

_____

_____

Is there anything else that you would like to make note of?

_____

_____

WEEKLY QUESTIONS   DATE   /   /

List two situations that you feel proud of this week, along with
the corresponding soft skill(s) that you demonstrated.

Tip: Reference the "soft-skills brainstorming page" for a refresher!

SITUATION   **SKILL(S)**

01

_____   _____

_____   _____

_____

_____

_____

02

_____   _____

_____   _____

_____

_____

_____

What challenge or unexpected hurdle did you face this week?

_____

_____

_____

_____

Did you have a memorable and/or difficult interaction with someone? What happened?

_____

_____

_____

_____

_____

Why are you grateful for this experience?

_____

_____

_____

_____

_____

In what way did you lend a helping hand, take on extra work, or otherwise go above and beyond?

_____

_____

_____

_____

_____

Is there anything else that you would like to make note of?

_____

_____

WEEKLY QUESTIONS

List two situations that you feel proud of this week, along with
the corresponding soft skill(s) that you demonstrated.

Tip: Reference the "soft-skills brainstorming page" for a refresher!

SITUATION   **SKILL(S)**

01

_____   _____

_____   _____

_____

_____

_____

02

_____   _____

_____   _____

_____

_____

_____

What challenge or unexpected hurdle did you face this week?

_____

_____

_____

_____

Did you have a memorable and/or difficult interaction with someone? What happened?

_____

_____

_____

_____

_____

Why are you grateful for this experience?

_____

_____

_____

_____

_____

In what way did you lend a helping hand, take on extra work, or otherwise go above and beyond?

_____

_____

_____

_____

_____

Is there anything else that you would like to make note of?

_____

_____

WEEKLY QUESTIONS

DATE   /   /

List two situations that you feel proud of this week, along with
the corresponding soft skill(s) that you demonstrated.
Tip: Reference the "soft-skills brainstorming page" for a refresher!

SITUATION   SKILL(S)

01
_____   _____

_____   _____

_____

_____

_____

02
_____   _____

_____   _____

_____

_____

_____

What challenge or unexpected hurdle did you face this week?

_____

_____

_____

_____

Did you have a memorable and/or difficult interaction with someone? What happened?

_____

_____

_____

_____

_____

Why are you grateful for this experience?

_____

_____

_____

_____

_____

In what way did you lend a helping hand, take on extra work, or otherwise go above and beyond?

_____

_____

_____

_____

_____

Is there anything else that you would like to make note of?

_____

_____

WEEKLY QUESTIONS

DATE / /

List two situations that you feel proud of this week, along with
the corresponding soft skill(s) that you demonstrated.

Tip: Reference the "soft-skills brainstorming page" for a refresher!

SITUATION   **SKILL(S)**

01
_____   _____

_____   _____

_____

_____

_____

02
_____   _____

_____   _____

_____

_____

_____

What challenge or unexpected hurdle did you face this week?

_____

_____

_____

_____

Did you have a memorable and/or difficult interaction with someone? What happened?

_____

_____

_____

_____

_____

Why are you grateful for this experience?

_____

_____

_____

_____

_____

In what way did you lend a helping hand, take on extra work, or otherwise go above and beyond?

_____

_____

_____

_____

_____

Is there anything else that you would like to make note of?

_____

_____

05 **MONTHLY QUESTIONS**

DATE   /   /

Describe a project, task, or situation that you are particularly proud of this month.

_____

_____

_____

_____

_____

_____

_____

_____

_____

_____

_____

Can you tie a metric to something that you did or contributed to somehow?

_____

_____

_____

_____

What did you do that was out of your comfort zone?

_____

_____

_____

_____

_____

Did you face an ambiguous situation? How did you move forward?

_____

_____

_____

_____

_____

Did you help someone to see a different angle, idea, or approach to a situation?

_____

_____

_____

_____

_____

Is there anything else that you would like to make note of?

_____

_____

WEEKLY QUESTIONS

List two situations that you feel proud of this week, along with
the corresponding soft skill(s) that you demonstrated.
Tip: Reference the "soft-skills brainstorming page" for a refresher!

SITUATION   **SKILL(S)**

01

_____   _____

_____   _____

_____

_____

_____

02

_____   _____

_____   _____

_____

_____

_____

What challenge or unexpected hurdle did you face this week?

_____

_____

_____

_____

Did you have a memorable and/or difficult interaction with someone? What happened?

_____

_____

_____

_____

_____

Why are you grateful for this experience?

_____

_____

_____

_____

In what way did you lend a helping hand, take on extra work, or otherwise go above and beyond?

_____

_____

_____

_____

_____

Is there anything else that you would like to make note of?

_____

_____

WEEKLY QUESTIONS

DATE ___ / ___ / ___

List two situations that you feel proud of this week, along with
the corresponding soft skill(s) that you demonstrated.
Tip: Reference the "soft-skills brainstorming page" for a refresher!

SITUATION   **SKILL(S)**

01
_____   _____

_____   _____

_____

_____

_____

02
_____   _____

_____   _____

_____

_____

_____

What challenge or unexpected hurdle did you face this week?

_____

_____

_____

_____

Did you have a memorable and/or difficult interaction with someone? What happened?

_____

_____

_____

_____

_____

Why are you grateful for this experience?

_____

_____

_____

_____

_____

In what way did you lend a helping hand, take on extra work, or otherwise go above and beyond?

_____

_____

_____

_____

_____

Is there anything else that you would like to make note of?

_____

_____

WEEKLY QUESTIONS

List two situations that you feel proud of this week, along with the corresponding soft skill(s) that you demonstrated.

Tip: Reference the "soft-skills brainstorming page" for a refresher!

SITUATION   **SKILL(S)**

01
_____   _____

_____   _____

_____

_____

_____

02
_____   _____

_____   _____

_____

_____

_____

What challenge or unexpected hurdle did you face this week?
_____

_____

_____

_____

Did you have a memorable and/or difficult interaction with someone? What happened?

_____

_____

_____

_____

_____

Why are you grateful for this experience?

_____

_____

_____

_____

_____

In what way did you lend a helping hand, take on extra work, or otherwise go above and beyond?

_____

_____

_____

_____

_____

Is there anything else that you would like to make note of?

_____

_____

List two situations that you feel proud of this week, along with
the corresponding soft skill(s) that you demonstrated.

Tip: Reference the "soft-skills brainstorming page" for a refresher!

SITUATION   **SKILL(S)**

01

_____   _____

_____   _____

_____

_____

_____

02

_____   _____

_____   _____

_____

_____

_____

What challenge or unexpected hurdle did you face this week?

_____

_____

_____

_____

Did you have a memorable and/or difficult interaction with someone? What happened?

_____

_____

_____

_____

_____

Why are you grateful for this experience?

_____

_____

_____

_____

_____

In what way did you lend a helping hand, take on extra work, or otherwise go above and beyond?

_____

_____

_____

_____

_____

Is there anything else that you would like to make note of?

_____

_____

MONTHLY QUESTIONS

DATE / /

Describe a project, task, or situation that you are particularly proud of this month.

_____

_____

_____

_____

_____

_____

_____

_____

_____

_____

_____

Can you tie a metric to something that you did or contributed to somehow?

_____

_____

_____

_____

What did you do that was out of your comfort zone?

_____

_____

_____

_____

_____

Did you face an ambiguous situation? How did you move forward?

_____

_____

_____

_____

_____

Did you help someone to see a different angle, idea, or approach to a situation?

_____

_____

_____

_____

_____

Is there anything else that you would like to make note of?

_____

_____

SIX MONTHS COMPLETE

Congratulations! You now have over 150 incredible work experiences written down for safekeeping. *You're a rockstar!*

List two situations that you feel proud of this week, along with the corresponding soft skill(s) that you demonstrated.

Tip: Reference the "soft-skills brainstorming page" for a refresher!

SITUATION　　　　　　　　　　　　　　　**SKILL(S)**

01
_____　　_____

_____　　_____

_____

_____

_____

02
_____　　_____

_____　　_____

_____

_____

_____

What challenge or unexpected hurdle did you face this week?

_____

_____

_____

_____

Did you have a memorable and/or difficult interaction with someone? What happened?

_____

_____

_____

_____

_____

Why are you grateful for this experience?

_____

_____

_____

_____

_____

In what way did you lend a helping hand, take on extra work, or otherwise go above and beyond?

_____

_____

_____

_____

_____

Is there anything else that you would like to make note of?

_____

_____

WEEKLY QUESTIONS

List two situations that you feel proud of this week, along with
the corresponding soft skill(s) that you demonstrated.

Tip: Reference the "soft-skills brainstorming page" for a refresher!

SITUATION   **SKILL(S)**

01 _____   _____

_____   _____

_____

_____

_____

02 _____   _____

_____   _____

_____

_____

_____

What challenge or unexpected hurdle did you face this week?

_____

_____

_____

_____

Did you have a memorable and/or difficult interaction with someone? What happened?

_____

_____

_____

_____

_____

Why are you grateful for this experience?

_____

_____

_____

_____

_____

In what way did you lend a helping hand, take on extra work, or otherwise go above and beyond?

_____

_____

_____

_____

_____

Is there anything else that you would like to make note of?

_____

_____

WEEKLY QUESTIONS

DATE / /

List two situations that you feel proud of this week, along with the corresponding soft skill(s) that you demonstrated.

Tip: Reference the "soft-skills brainstorming page" for a refresher!

SITUATION   **SKILL(S)**

01 _____   _____

_____   _____

_____

_____

_____

02 _____   _____

_____   _____

_____

_____

_____

What challenge or unexpected hurdle did you face this week?

_____

_____

_____

_____

Did you have a memorable and/or difficult interaction with someone? What happened?

_____

_____

_____

_____

_____

Why are you grateful for this experience?

_____

_____

_____

_____

_____

In what way did you lend a helping hand, take on extra work, or otherwise go above and beyond?

_____

_____

_____

_____

Is there anything else that you would like to make note of?

_____

_____

WEEKLY QUESTIONS

List two situations that you feel proud of this week, along with the corresponding soft skill(s) that you demonstrated.

Tip: Reference the "soft-skills brainstorming page" for a refresher!

SITUATION   **SKILL(S)**

01 _____   _____

_____   _____

_____

_____

_____

02 _____   _____

_____   _____

_____

_____

_____

What challenge or unexpected hurdle did you face this week?

_____

_____

_____

_____

Did you have a memorable and/or difficult interaction with someone? What happened?

_____

_____

_____

_____

_____

Why are you grateful for this experience?

_____

_____

_____

_____

_____

In what way did you lend a helping hand, take on extra work, or otherwise go above and beyond?

_____

_____

_____

_____

_____

Is there anything else that you would like to make note of?

_____

_____

07 MONTHLY QUESTIONS

DATE / /

Describe a project, task, or situation that you are particularly proud of this month.

_____

_____

_____

_____

_____

_____

_____

_____

_____

_____

_____

_____

Can you tie a metric to something that you did or contributed to somehow?

_____

_____

_____

_____

_____

What did you do that was out of your comfort zone?

_____

_____

_____

_____

_____

Did you face an ambiguous situation? How did you move forward?

_____

_____

_____

_____

_____

Did you help someone to see a different angle, idea, or approach to a situation?

_____

_____

_____

_____

_____

Is there anything else that you would like to make note of?

_____

_____

WEEKLY QUESTIONS

List two situations that you feel proud of this week, along with
the corresponding soft skill(s) that you demonstrated.

Tip: Reference the "soft-skills brainstorming page" for a refresher!

SITUATION   **SKILL(S)**

01 _____   _____

_____   _____

_____

_____

_____

02 _____   _____

_____   _____

_____

_____

_____

What challenge or unexpected hurdle did you face this week?

_____

_____

_____

_____

Did you have a memorable and/or difficult interaction with someone? What happened?

_____

_____

_____

_____

_____

Why are you grateful for this experience?

_____

_____

_____

_____

_____

In what way did you lend a helping hand, take on extra work, or otherwise go above and beyond?

_____

_____

_____

_____

_____

Is there anything else that you would like to make note of?

_____

_____

WEEKLY QUESTIONS

DATE / /

List two situations that you feel proud of this week, along with
the corresponding soft skill(s) that you demonstrated.

Tip: Reference the "soft-skills brainstorming page" for a refresher!

SITUATION   **SKILL(S)**

01 _____   _____

_____   _____

_____

_____

_____

02 _____   _____

_____   _____

_____

_____

_____

What challenge or unexpected hurdle did you face this week?

_____

_____

_____

_____

Did you have a memorable and/or difficult interaction with someone? What happened?

_____

_____

_____

_____

_____

Why are you grateful for this experience?

_____

_____

_____

_____

_____

In what way did you lend a helping hand, take on extra work, or otherwise go above and beyond?

_____

_____

_____

_____

_____

Is there anything else that you would like to make note of?

_____

_____

WEEKLY QUESTIONS   DATE   /   /

List two situations that you feel proud of this week, along with
the corresponding soft skill(s) that you demonstrated.

Tip: Reference the "soft-skills brainstorming page" for a refresher!

SITUATION   **SKILL(S)**

01
_____   _____

_____   _____

_____

_____

_____

02
_____   _____

_____   _____

_____

_____

_____

What challenge or unexpected hurdle did you face this week?

_____

_____

_____

_____

Did you have a memorable and/or difficult interaction with someone? What happened?

_____

_____

_____

_____

_____

Why are you grateful for this experience?

_____

_____

_____

_____

_____

In what way did you lend a helping hand, take on extra work, or otherwise go above and beyond?

_____

_____

_____

_____

_____

Is there anything else that you would like to make note of?

_____

_____

WEEKLY QUESTIONS

List two situations that you feel proud of this week, along with the corresponding soft skill(s) that you demonstrated.

Tip: Reference the "soft-skills brainstorming page" for a refresher!

SITUATION   **SKILL(S)**

01 _____   _____

_____   _____

_____

_____

_____

02 _____   _____

_____   _____

_____

_____

_____

What challenge or unexpected hurdle did you face this week?

_____

_____

_____

_____

Did you have a memorable and/or difficult interaction with someone? What happened?

_____

_____

_____

_____

_____

Why are you grateful for this experience?

_____

_____

_____

_____

_____

In what way did you lend a helping hand, take on extra work, or otherwise go above and beyond?

_____

_____

_____

_____

_____

Is there anything else that you would like to make note of?

_____

_____

08 MONTHLY QUESTIONS

DATE   /   /

Describe a project, task, or situation that you are particularly proud of this month.

_____

_____

_____

_____

_____

_____

_____

_____

_____

_____

Can you tie a metric to something that you did or contributed to somehow?

_____

_____

_____

_____

What did you do that was out of your comfort zone?

_____

_____

_____

_____

_____

Did you face an ambiguous situation? How did you move forward?

_____

_____

_____

_____

Did you help someone to see a different angle, idea, or approach to a situation?

_____

_____

_____

_____

Is there anything else that you would like to make note of?

_____

_____

WEEKLY QUESTIONS

List two situations that you feel proud of this week, along with
the corresponding soft skill(s) that you demonstrated.

Tip: Reference the "soft-skills brainstorming page" for a refresher!

SITUATION   **SKILL(S)**

01
_____   _____

_____   _____

_____

_____

_____

02
_____   _____

_____   _____

_____

_____

What challenge or unexpected hurdle did you face this week?

_____

_____

_____

_____

Did you have a memorable and/or difficult interaction with someone? What happened?

_____

_____

_____

_____

_____

Why are you grateful for this experience?

_____

_____

_____

_____

_____

In what way did you lend a helping hand, take on extra work, or otherwise go above and beyond?

_____

_____

_____

_____

_____

Is there anything else that you would like to make note of?

_____

_____

WEEKLY QUESTIONS

List two situations that you feel proud of this week, along with the corresponding soft skill(s) that you demonstrated.

Tip: Reference the "soft-skills brainstorming page" for a refresher!

SITUATION   **SKILL(S)**

01 _____   _____

_____   _____

_____

_____

_____

02 _____   _____

_____   _____

_____

_____

_____

What challenge or unexpected hurdle did you face this week?

_____

_____

_____

_____

Did you have a memorable and/or difficult interaction with someone? What happened?

_____

_____

_____

_____

_____

Why are you grateful for this experience?

_____

_____

_____

_____

_____

In what way did you lend a helping hand, take on extra work, or otherwise go above and beyond?

_____

_____

_____

_____

_____

Is there anything else that you would like to make note of?

_____

_____

WEEKLY QUESTIONS

List two situations that you feel proud of this week, along with the corresponding soft skill(s) that you demonstrated.

Tip: Reference the "soft-skills brainstorming page" for a refresher!

SITUATION   **SKILL(S)**

01 _____   _____

_____   _____

_____

_____

_____

02 _____   _____

_____   _____

_____

_____

_____

What challenge or unexpected hurdle did you face this week?

_____

_____

_____

_____

Did you have a memorable and/or difficult interaction with someone? What happened?

_____

_____

_____

_____

_____

Why are you grateful for this experience?

_____

_____

_____

_____

_____

In what way did you lend a helping hand, take on extra work, or otherwise go above and beyond?

_____

_____

_____

_____

_____

Is there anything else that you would like to make note of?

_____

_____

WEEKLY QUESTIONS

DATE   /   /

List two situations that you feel proud of this week, along with
the corresponding soft skill(s) that you demonstrated.
Tip: Reference the "soft-skills brainstorming page" for a refresher!

SITUATION   **SKILL(S)**

01 _____   _____

_____   _____

_____

_____

_____

02 _____   _____

_____   _____

_____

_____

_____

What challenge or unexpected hurdle did you face this week?

_____

_____

_____

_____

Did you have a memorable and/or difficult interaction with someone? What happened?

_____

_____

_____

_____

_____

Why are you grateful for this experience?

_____

_____

_____

_____

_____

In what way did you lend a helping hand, take on extra work, or otherwise go above and beyond?

_____

_____

_____

_____

_____

Is there anything else that you would like to make note of?

_____

_____

MONTHLY QUESTIONS

DATE / /

Describe a project, task, or situation that you are particularly proud of this month.

_____

_____

_____

_____

_____

_____

_____

_____

_____

_____

_____

Can you tie a metric to something that you did or contributed to somehow?

_____

_____

_____

_____

_____

What did you do that was out of your comfort zone?

_____

_____

_____

_____

_____

Did you face an ambiguous situation? How did you move forward?

_____

_____

_____

_____

Did you help someone to see a different angle, idea, or approach to a situation?

_____

_____

_____

_____

Is there anything else that you would like to make note of?

_____

_____

WEEKLY QUESTIONS

List two situations that you feel proud of this week, along with the corresponding soft skill(s) that you demonstrated.

Tip: Reference the "soft-skills brainstorming page" for a refresher!

SITUATION   **SKILL(S)**

01
_____   _____

_____   _____

_____

_____

_____

02
_____   _____

_____   _____

_____

_____

_____

What challenge or unexpected hurdle did you face this week?

_____

_____

_____

_____

Did you have a memorable and/or difficult interaction with someone? What happened?

_____

_____

_____

_____

_____

Why are you grateful for this experience?

_____

_____

_____

_____

_____

In what way did you lend a helping hand, take on extra work, or otherwise go above and beyond?

_____

_____

_____

_____

_____

Is there anything else that you would like to make note of?

_____

_____

WEEKLY QUESTIONS

List two situations that you feel proud of this week, along with the corresponding soft skill(s) that you demonstrated.

Tip: Reference the "soft-skills brainstorming page" for a refresher!

SITUATION   **SKILL(S)**

01 _____   _____

_____   _____

_____

_____

_____

02 _____   _____

_____   _____

_____

_____

_____

What challenge or unexpected hurdle did you face this week?

_____

_____

_____

_____

Did you have a memorable and/or difficult interaction with someone? What happened?

_____

_____

_____

_____

_____

Why are you grateful for this experience?

_____

_____

_____

_____

In what way did you lend a helping hand, take on extra work, or otherwise go above and beyond?

_____

_____

_____

_____

Is there anything else that you would like to make note of?

_____

_____

WEEKLY QUESTIONS

List two situations that you feel proud of this week, along with the corresponding soft skill(s) that you demonstrated.

Tip: Reference the "soft-skills brainstorming page" for a refresher!

SITUATION   **SKILL(S)**

01
_____   _____

_____   _____

_____

_____

_____

02
_____   _____

_____   _____

_____

_____

What challenge or unexpected hurdle did you face this week?

_____

_____

_____

_____

Did you have a memorable and/or difficult interaction with someone? What happened?

_____

_____

_____

_____

_____

Why are you grateful for this experience?

_____

_____

_____

_____

_____

In what way did you lend a helping hand, take on extra work, or otherwise go above and beyond?

_____

_____

_____

_____

_____

Is there anything else that you would like to make note of?

_____

_____

WEEKLY QUESTIONS

List two situations that you feel proud of this week, along with
the corresponding soft skill(s) that you demonstrated.
Tip: Reference the "soft-skills brainstorming page" for a refresher!

SITUATION   **SKILL(S)**

01
_____   _____

_____   _____

_____

_____

_____

02
_____   _____

_____   _____

_____

_____

_____

What challenge or unexpected hurdle did you face this week?

_____

_____

_____

_____

Did you have a memorable and/or difficult interaction with someone? What happened?

_____

_____

_____

_____

_____

Why are you grateful for this experience?

_____

_____

_____

_____

_____

In what way did you lend a helping hand, take on extra work, or otherwise go above and beyond?

_____

_____

_____

_____

_____

Is there anything else that you would like to make note of?

_____

_____

MONTHLY QUESTIONS

DATE / /

Describe a project, task, or situation that you are particularly proud of this month.

_____

_____

_____

_____

_____

_____

_____

_____

_____

_____

Can you tie a metric to something that you did or contributed to somehow?

_____

_____

_____

_____

What did you do that was out of your comfort zone?

_____

_____

_____

_____

_____

Did you face an ambiguous situation? How did you move forward?

_____

_____

_____

_____

_____

Did you help someone to see a different angle, idea, or approach to a situation?

_____

_____

_____

_____

_____

Is there anything else that you would like to make note of?

_____

_____

WEEKLY QUESTIONS

DATE / /

List two situations that you feel proud of this week, along with the corresponding soft skill(s) that you demonstrated.

Tip: Reference the "soft-skills brainstorming page" for a refresher!

SITUATION	SKILL(S)
01	

SITUATION	SKILL(S)
02	

What challenge or unexpected hurdle did you face this week?

Did you have a memorable and/or difficult interaction with someone? What happened?

_____

_____

_____

_____

_____

Why are you grateful for this experience?

_____

_____

_____

_____

_____

In what way did you lend a helping hand, take on extra work, or otherwise go above and beyond?

_____

_____

_____

_____

_____

Is there anything else that you would like to make note of?

_____

_____

WEEKLY QUESTIONS

List two situations that you feel proud of this week, along with
the corresponding soft skill(s) that you demonstrated.

Tip: Reference the "soft-skills brainstorming page" for a refresher!

SITUATION   **SKILL(S)**

01 _____   _____

_____   _____

_____

_____

_____

02 _____   _____

_____   _____

_____

_____

What challenge or unexpected hurdle did you face this week?

_____

_____

_____

_____

Did you have a memorable and/or difficult interaction with someone? What happened?

_____

_____

_____

_____

_____

Why are you grateful for this experience?

_____

_____

_____

_____

_____

In what way did you lend a helping hand, take on extra work, or otherwise go above and beyond?

_____

_____

_____

_____

_____

Is there anything else that you would like to make note of?

_____

_____

WEEKLY QUESTIONS

List two situations that you feel proud of this week, along with
the corresponding soft skill(s) that you demonstrated.

Tip: Reference the "soft-skills brainstorming page" for a refresher!

SITUATION   **SKILL(S)**

01
_____   _____

_____   _____

_____

_____

_____

02
_____   _____

_____   _____

_____

_____

_____

What challenge or unexpected hurdle did you face this week?

_____

_____

_____

_____

Did you have a memorable and/or difficult interaction with someone? What happened?

_____

_____

_____

_____

_____

Why are you grateful for this experience?

_____

_____

_____

_____

In what way did you lend a helping hand, take on extra work, or otherwise go above and beyond?

_____

_____

_____

_____

Is there anything else that you would like to make note of?

_____

_____

WEEKLY QUESTIONS

List two situations that you feel proud of this week, along with
the corresponding soft skill(s) that you demonstrated.

Tip: Reference the "soft-skills brainstorming page" for a refresher!

SITUATION   **SKILL(S)**

01

_____   _____

_____   _____

_____

_____

_____

02

_____   _____

_____   _____

_____

_____

_____

What challenge or unexpected hurdle did you face this week?

_____

_____

_____

_____

Did you have a memorable and/or difficult interaction with someone? What happened?

_____

_____

_____

_____

_____

Why are you grateful for this experience?

_____

_____

_____

_____

_____

In what way did you lend a helping hand, take on extra work, or otherwise go above and beyond?

_____

_____

_____

_____

_____

Is there anything else that you would like to make note of?

_____

_____

 **DATE** / /

Describe a project, task, or situation that you are particularly proud of this month.

_____

_____

_____

_____

_____

_____

_____

_____

_____

_____

_____

_____

Can you tie a metric to something that you did or contributed to somehow?

_____

_____

_____

_____

_____

What did you do that was out of your comfort zone?

_____

_____

_____

_____

_____

Did you face an ambiguous situation? How did you move forward?

_____

_____

_____

_____

_____

Did you help someone to see a different angle, idea, or approach to a situation?

_____

_____

_____

_____

_____

Is there anything else that you would like to make note of?

_____

_____

WEEKLY QUESTIONS

DATE / /

List two situations that you feel proud of this week, along with
the corresponding soft skill(s) that you demonstrated.

Tip: Reference the "soft-skills brainstorming page" for a refresher!

SITUATION   **SKILL(S)**

01 _____   _____

_____   _____

_____

_____

_____

02 _____   _____

_____   _____

_____

_____

_____

What challenge or unexpected hurdle did you face this week?

_____

_____

_____

_____

Did you have a memorable and/or difficult interaction with someone? What happened?

_____

_____

_____

_____

Why are you grateful for this experience?

_____

_____

_____

_____

In what way did you lend a helping hand, take on extra work, or otherwise go above and beyond?

_____

_____

_____

_____

Is there anything else that you would like to make note of?

_____

_____

List two situations that you feel proud of this week, along with
the corresponding soft skill(s) that you demonstrated.

Tip: Reference the "soft-skills brainstorming page" for a refresher!

SITUATION   **SKILL(S)**

01 _____   _____

_____   _____

_____

_____

_____

02 _____   _____

_____   _____

_____

_____

_____

What challenge or unexpected hurdle did you face this week?

_____

_____

_____

_____

Did you have a memorable and/or difficult interaction with someone? What happened?

_____

_____

_____

_____

_____

Why are you grateful for this experience?

_____

_____

_____

_____

In what way did you lend a helping hand, take on extra work, or otherwise go above and beyond?

_____

_____

_____

_____

Is there anything else that you would like to make note of?

_____

_____

WEEKLY QUESTIONS

List two situations that you feel proud of this week, along with the corresponding soft skill(s) that you demonstrated.

Tip: Reference the "soft-skills brainstorming page" for a refresher!

SITUATION   **SKILL(S)**

01 _____   _____

_____   _____

_____

_____

_____

02 _____   _____

_____   _____

_____

_____

_____

What challenge or unexpected hurdle did you face this week?

_____

_____

_____

_____

Did you have a memorable and/or difficult interaction with someone? What happened?

_____

_____

_____

_____

_____

Why are you grateful for this experience?

_____

_____

_____

_____

In what way did you lend a helping hand, take on extra work, or otherwise go above and beyond?

_____

_____

_____

_____

Is there anything else that you would like to make note of?

_____

_____

WEEKLY QUESTIONS

List two situations that you feel proud of this week, along with
the corresponding soft skill(s) that you demonstrated.

Tip: Reference the "soft-skills brainstorming page" for a refresher!

SITUATION   **SKILL(S)**

01
_____   _____

_____   _____

_____

_____

_____

02
_____   _____

_____   _____

_____

_____

_____

What challenge or unexpected hurdle did you face this week?

_____

_____

_____

_____

Did you have a memorable and/or difficult interaction with someone? What happened?

_____

_____

_____

_____

_____

Why are you grateful for this experience?

_____

_____

_____

_____

In what way did you lend a helping hand, take on extra work, or otherwise go above and beyond?

_____

_____

_____

_____

_____

Is there anything else that you would like to make note of?

_____

_____

Describe a project, task, or situation that you are particularly proud of this month.

_____

_____

_____

_____

_____

_____

_____

_____

_____

_____

_____

Can you tie a metric to something that you did or contributed to somehow?

_____

_____

_____

_____

_____

What did you do that was out of your comfort zone?

_____

_____

_____

_____

_____

Did you face an ambiguous situation? How did you move forward?

_____

_____

_____

_____

_____

Did you help someone to see a different angle, idea, or approach to a situation?

_____

_____

_____

_____

_____

Is there anything else that you would like to make note of?

_____

_____

WEEKLY QUESTIONS

DATE / /

List two situations that you feel proud of this week, along with the corresponding soft skill(s) that you demonstrated.

Tip: Reference the "soft-skills brainstorming page" for a refresher!

SITUATION   **SKILL(S)**

01
_____   _____

_____   _____

_____

_____

_____

02
_____   _____

_____   _____

_____

_____

_____

What challenge or unexpected hurdle did you face this week?

_____

_____

_____

_____

Did you have a memorable and/or difficult interaction with someone? What happened?

_____

_____

_____

_____

_____

Why are you grateful for this experience?

_____

_____

_____

_____

_____

In what way did you lend a helping hand, take on extra work, or otherwise go above and beyond?

_____

_____

_____

_____

_____

Is there anything else that you would like to make note of?

_____

_____

WEEKLY QUESTIONS

DATE / /

List two situations that you feel proud of this week, along with
the corresponding soft skill(s) that you demonstrated.

Tip: Reference the "soft-skills brainstorming page" for a refresher!

SITUATION   **SKILL(S)**

01
_____   _____

_____   _____

_____

_____

_____

02
_____   _____

_____   _____

_____

_____

_____

What challenge or unexpected hurdle did you face this week?

_____

_____

_____

_____

Did you have a memorable and/or difficult interaction with someone? What happened?

_____

_____

_____

_____

_____

Why are you grateful for this experience?

_____

_____

_____

_____

_____

In what way did you lend a helping hand, take on extra work, or otherwise go above and beyond?

_____

_____

_____

_____

_____

Is there anything else that you would like to make note of?

_____

_____

WEEKLY QUESTIONS

DATE   /   /

List two situations that you feel proud of this week, along with the corresponding soft skill(s) that you demonstrated.
Tip: Reference the "soft-skills brainstorming page" for a refresher!

SITUATION   **SKILL(S)**

01
_____   _____

_____   _____

_____

_____

_____

02
_____   _____

_____   _____

_____

_____

What challenge or unexpected hurdle did you face this week?

_____

_____

_____

_____

Did you have a memorable and/or difficult interaction with someone? What happened?

_____

_____

_____

_____

_____

Why are you grateful for this experience?

_____

_____

_____

_____

_____

In what way did you lend a helping hand, take on extra work, or otherwise go above and beyond?

_____

_____

_____

_____

_____

Is there anything else that you would like to make note of?

_____

_____

WEEKLY QUESTIONS

DATE / /

List two situations that you feel proud of this week, along with the corresponding soft skill(s) that you demonstrated.

Tip: Reference the "soft-skills brainstorming page" for a refresher!

SITUATION   **SKILL(S)**

01

_____   _____

_____   _____

_____

_____

_____

02

_____   _____

_____   _____

_____

_____

_____

What challenge or unexpected hurdle did you face this week?

_____

_____

_____

_____

Did you have a memorable and/or difficult interaction with someone? What happened?

_____

_____

_____

_____

_____

Why are you grateful for this experience?

_____

_____

_____

_____

_____

In what way did you lend a helping hand, take on extra work, or otherwise go above and beyond?

_____

_____

_____

_____

_____

Is there anything else that you would like to make note of?

_____

_____

BONUS MONTH

DATE / /

Describe a project, task, or situation that you are particularly proud of this month.

_____

_____

_____

_____

_____

_____

_____

_____

_____

_____

Can you tie a metric to something that you did or contributed to somehow?

_____

_____

_____

_____

_____

What did you do that was out of your comfort zone?

_____

_____

_____

_____

_____

Did you face an ambiguous situation? How did you move forward?

_____

_____

_____

_____

_____

Did you help someone to see a different angle, idea, or approach to a situation?

_____

_____

_____

_____

_____

Is there anything else that you would like to make note of?

_____

_____

YEAR-IN-REVIEW QUESTIONS

What are your career goals today?

...Maybe they're the same as one year ago, or perhaps they have evolved!

_____

_____

_____

_____

_____

_____

_____

Reflecting on your professional weaknesses, how have they improved over the last year?

...For example, if you felt that you were too empathetic, maybe you read a couple

of self-help books or faced a handful of issues that required you to push past your

feelings in order to get the job done.

_____

_____

_____

_____

_____

_____

_____

In what way(s) have your weaknesses evolved into strengths?

...Maybe this new and improved empathy grounds you in your decision-making

process, causing you to assess all angles of a situation before making your move.

Tie a metric to something that you've achieved this year (or contributed to majorly).

...This could be your overall productivity metric, the total number of articles you

have edited, the number of customer support tickets you have closed, the number

of team members that you have hired, the total value of your sales, etc.

Describe a project where you assisted in innovation, automation, or system improvement for the company.

...Perhaps you helped implement new (and more accurate) software, instituted an

ordering process for office supplies, created a series of templates for your team,

found a way to automate appointment reminders instead of manually calling

people, etc.

What's the *biggest* mistake you made this year?

...I forgot about an important meeting with a high-profile client, and they threatened

to take their business elsewhere.

What did you learn from this experience?

...I need to be better organized, especially when it comes to meetings.

_____

_____

_____

_____

_____

_____

_____

How have you changed the way you operate to prevent similar instances in the future?

...I started to properly use the company calendar and boardroom system,

revealing that I actually love when technology does the work for me. Now I use

a calendar for my personal life, too! I haven't missed a meeting since that day;

in fact, I am always early!

_____

_____

_____

_____

_____

Which two co-workers (or clients) did you make the biggest impact on this year?

**CO-WORKER/
CLIENT**

HOW I MADE A DIFFERENCE

01 Sheela

I was there for her whenever she felt overwhelmed.

_____

_____

02 _____

_____

_____

_____

Which three accomplishments are you most proud of this year?

01   ...I executed a two-month product inventory audit and completed it ahead

of schedule. I proved to myself that I could stay accountable, focused, and in

control of my timeline on large projects.

02 _____

_____

_____

03 _____

_____

_____

SOFT-SKILLS BRAINSTORMING PAGE

ADAPTABILITY / PRIORITIZATION / ORGANIZATION / TEAMWORK / AGILITY

INITIATIVE / CUSTOMER SERVICE / DECISION MAKING / DEPENDABILITY

ATTENTION TO DETAIL / INDEPENDENCE / INNOVATION / COLLABORATION

LEADERSHIP / NEGOTIATION / CONFLICT RESOLUTION / PERSEVERANCE

PEOPLE MANAGEMENT / PLANNING / PRESENTATION / INTEGRITY / FOCUS

PROACTIVITY / PROBLEM SOLVING / PROFESSIONALISM / TIME MANAGEMENT

RESOURCEFULNESS / STRESS MANAGEMENT / PATIENCE / RELIABILITY

VERSATILITY / VERBAL COMMUNICATION / WRITTEN COMMUNICATION

TRAINING / WORK ETHIC / ACTIVE LISTENING / ANALYTICAL THINKING

ASSERTIVENESS / AUTOMATION / BRAINSTORMING / COMMITMENT / OPTIMISM

COACHING / COMPETITIVENESS / CONFIDENCE / GOAL SETTING / CREATIVITY

RESILIENCE / RESPONSIBILITY / RECEPTIVENESS TO FEEDBACK / RESULTS ORIENTED

CRITICAL THINKING / CULTURAL INTELLIGENCE / DELEGATION / DISCIPLINE

OPEN-MINDEDNESS / OUTSIDE-THE-BOX THINKING / PUBLIC SPEAKING / RESEARCH

DIPLOMACY / EFFICIENCY / EMOTIONAL INTELLIGENCE / EMPATHY / ENTHUSIASM

FRIENDLINESS / FLEXIBILITY / FORESIGHT / GENEROSITY / LISTENING

MEETING MANAGEMENT / MOTIVATING OTHERS / OBSERVATION / PERSISTENCE

COOPERATION / LOGICAL REASONING / MENTORING / PERSUASION

SCHEDULING / SELF MOTIVATION / TROUBLESHOOTING / TEAM PLAYER

TOLERANCE / TECHNOLOGICALLY SAVVY / HUMILITY / SYNERGISTIC ABILITIES

_____ / _____ / _____ / _____ / _____

NOTES

ABOUT THE AUTHOR

Prior to writing this book, Sydney worked in human resources, thus conducting hundreds of job interviews and performance reviews in the tech sector. It was then that she faced a glaring realization: Many people, especially early-career professionals, seriously sell themselves short.

Utilizing her experience in both conducting and attending job interviews and performance reviews, Sydney decided to translate her observations, knowledge, and insights into #realtalk, providing an actionable tool kit for helping ambitious professionals to reach their career goals faster.